MEGA ROBO BROS
ROBOT REVENGE

BY NEILL CAMERON

MEGA ROBO BROS!

Technology

14 March
by R. Krulwich, staff writer

Following their dramatic rescue of the
royal family from rogue palace guard-bots
in an apparent terrorist attack on Buckingham
Palace last year, sentient robots Alex and
Freddy Sharma have found themselves thrust
into the national spotlight. The world's only
legally recognised sentient robots, they serve
as agents of R.A.I.D. - Robotics Analysis,
Intelligence and Defence - defending the UK
from all manner of high-tech threats, while

Mega Robo Bros: Robot Revenge
is book 3 in the Mega Robo Bros Series:

Power Up
Double Threat
Robot Revenge
Meltdown

For Logan. Again. Obviously.

Mega Robo Bros: Robot Revenge
is a
DAVID FICKLING BOOK

The comics in this book were first published as
Mega Robo Revenge

First published in Great Britain in 2022 by
David Fickling Books,
31 Beaumont Street,
Oxford, OX1 2NP
www.davidficklingbooks.com

Text and illustrations © Neill Cameron, 2022
Cover design by Alison Gadsby, James Fraser and Paul Duffield.
Colour assistance by Alice Leclert.

978-1-78845-234-2
1 3 5 7 9 10 8 6 4 2

MIX
Paper from
responsible sources
FSC® C007785
FSC www.fsc.org

DAVID FICKLING BOOKS Reg. No. 8340307
A CIP catalogue record for this book is available
from the British Library.
Printed in Great Britain by Bell and Bain Ltd, Glasgow.

ROGUE
ATTACK

News // UK // London

Photo: AP

ALEX-
0021

TABLE OF CONTENTS

Chapter 1: 11

Chapter 2: 28

Chapter 3: 73

Chapter 4: 93

Chapter 5: 103

Bonus Materials: .174

BOT
XPO!

, staff writer

cenes of chaos at London's
O EXPO yesterday, after the
srupted by an attack from
nidentified robot.

ing a panel debate featuring
tor Baroness Fatima Farooq ar
e officer Nita Sharma, witnesse
e attack could have caused
ualties were it not for the heroi
ntient robots Alex and Freddy
e so-called 'Mega Robo Bros',
tending the event and managed to
ogue mechanoid.

re was significant and extensive
he Expo site, only a few minor injuries
ongst civilian bystanders at the event.

FREDDY'S AWESOME WORLD - NEW VIDEO!
2,026,899 views

*ROBOTICS ANALYSIS, INTELLIGENCE & DEFENCE

7

9

FREDDY, I'M ONLY LETTING YOU COME TO TAIA'S TO PLAY *KNIGHTS OF SHAMBALA* WITH US BECAUSE WE NEEDED A FOURTH, OKAY?

AND ALSO BECAUSE DAD THREW US OUT OF THE HOUSE.

HA!

I'M GOING TO *DESTROY* YOU AT IT!

I SWEAR, IF YOU EMBARRASS ME...

OHH I'LL *EMBARRASS* YOU ALL RIGHT – WHEN I TURN OUT TO BE TEN TIMES BETTER AT YOUR DUMB GAME THAN *YOU* ARE!

HUH.

THIS WAS CLEARLY A MISTAKE.

YOU'RE CLEARLY A MISTAKE!

UH... GUYS?

OH MY GOD, YOU ARE SO ANNOYING!

I KNOW YOU ARE, BUT WHAT AM I?

GUYS, SERIOUSLY. YOU MIGHT WANT TO SEE THIS.

WHAT IS IT, MIRA?

ALL MY FEEDS STARTED PINGING — THERE'S THIS VIDEO STREAM, IT'S POPPING UP EVERYWHERE...

...AND IT'S ABOUT YOU GUYS.

WHAT?

HEY, THAT'S ME!

LET ME SEE!

DUDE, DON'T GRAB.

...STREAMING LIVE FROM LONDON'S PICCADILLY CIRCUS!

AND WE'LL SAY IT AGAIN...

►LIVE!!!

ROBOTIX

THE "MEGA ROBO BROS"...

...ARE MEGA ROBO JOKES!

13

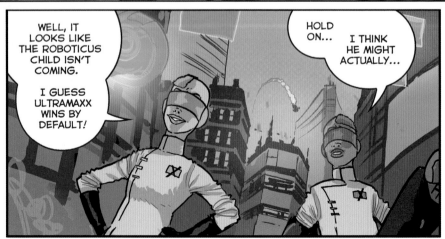

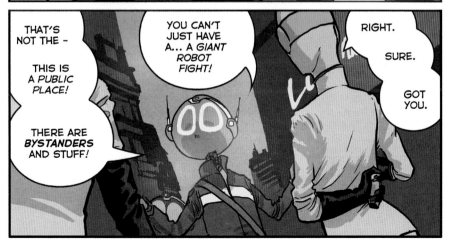

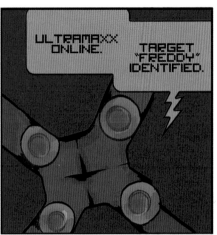

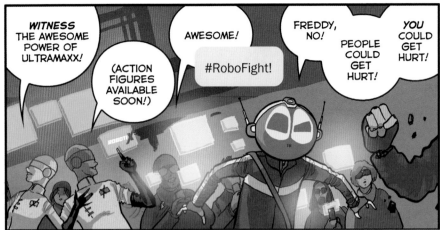

HONESTLY.

I *LITERALLY* JUST WANTED TO PLAY BOARD GAMES TODAY.

KRASHHH!!!

CHAPTER 2

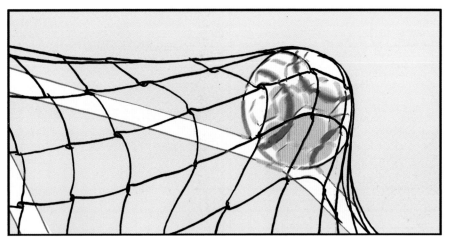

NICE *SHOT*, SHARMA!

ALL RIGHT, YOU'RE IN THE STARTING LINE-UP FOR SURE.

WHAT?

NO!

SIR, IT'S NOT *FAIR!* HE'S... HE'S *CHEATING!*

HE'S USING HIS *ROBOT POWERS* AND *STUFF!*

SIR, I WASN'T, HONEST.

I HAD MY STRENGTH AND SPEED DIALLED DOWN TO STANDARD HUMAN RANGE, AND –

AAAAND... MUSA!

...SORRY, ALEX.

41

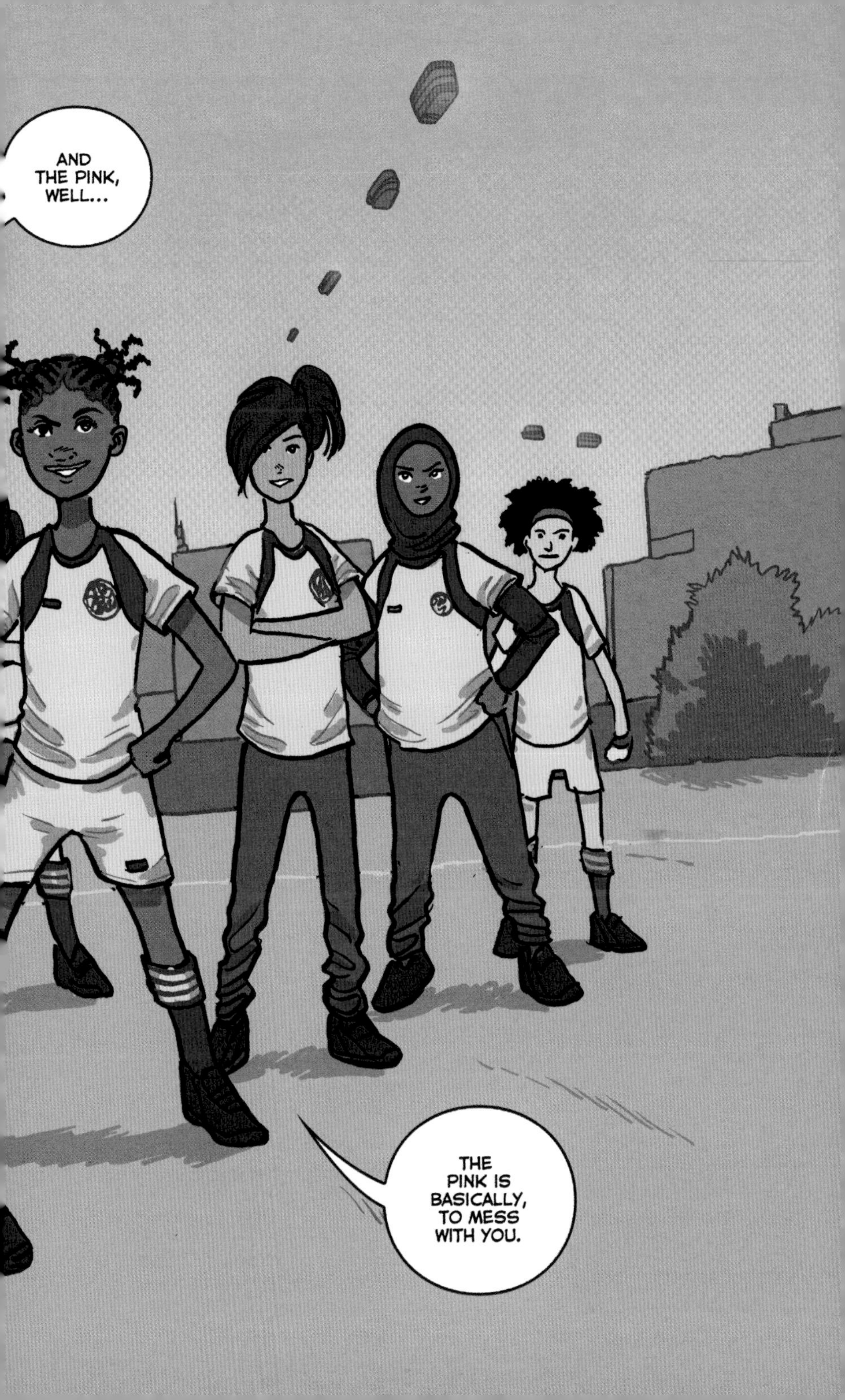
AND THE PINK, WELL...
THE PINK IS BASICALLY, TO MESS WITH YOU.

49

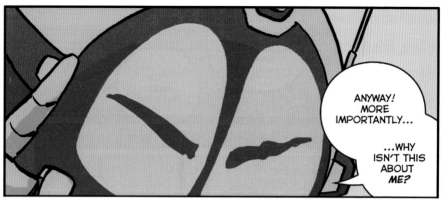

54

THURSDAY.

FETCH! GOOD BOY!

GOOD *DOG.*

FRIDAY.

THAT'S RIGHT, PLAY WITH THE STRING!

LIKE THE CAT THAT YOU CLEARLY ARE.

SATURDAY.

HE IS *LITERALLY* WOOFING.

WOOF!

THAT'S CIRCUM-STANTIAL!

CAT!

DOG!

CAT!

OH FOR...

CAN YOU GUYS JUST... *STOP?*

ALL THE TIME, *CAT! DOG! CAT! DOG!*

I'M *UNBELIEVABLY* BORED OF IT.

ALEX... WE'RE ONLY JOKING...

WELL, IT'S *DUMB!*

TRIKEY ISN'T A DOG *OR* A CAT.

HE'S A *ROBOT TRICERATOPS.*

OBVIOUSLY.

HE'S SOMETHING *NEW.*

WHY DO YOU HAVE TO... TO TRY AND STICK HIM INTO SOME NEAT BOX?

JUST SO IT'S EASIER FOR *YOU?*

WHAT *IS* THAT? IS IT A *HUMAN* THING?

BECAUSE I'M TELLING YOU, IT'S *DEEPLY* ANNOYING.

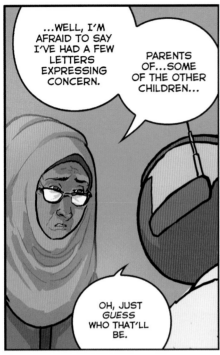

...WELL, I'M AFRAID TO SAY I'VE HAD A FEW LETTERS EXPRESSING CONCERN.

PARENTS OF...SOME OF THE OTHER CHILDREN...

OH, JUST *GUESS* WHO THAT'LL BE.

ALEX.

WELL! IT'S JAMAL AND HIS LITTLE GANG, ISN'T IT?

ALEX... YOU KNOW I CAN'T DISCUSS THAT.

WHY'S IT ANY OF THEIR BUSINESS?

WHY'S IT ANYONE'S BUSINESS?

ALEX!

YOU ARE IN YOUR HEADTEACHER'S OFFICE, AND YOU WILL SHOW SOME RESPECT!

APART FROM ANYTHING ELSE, THIS SCHOOL HAS A STRICT UNIFORM POLICY.

IF ONE OF THE PUPILS SUDDENLY DECIDED TO... DIE THEIR *HAIR* BRIGHT PINK, WE'D BE HAVING A VERY SIMILAR CONVERSATION.

FREDDY'S RED.

FREDDY'S RED, AND NOBODY'S EVER SAID *ANYTHING*.

ALEX...

I'D AVOID ALL THIS IF I COULD,

I HOPE YOU KNOW THAT.

BUT I HAVE TO TELL YOU, THERE'S BEEN TALK OF ORGANISING A PROTEST –

EVEN OF GETTING THE *PRESS* INVOLVED...

THIS IS *SO UNFAIR!*

...ALEX, I'M SORRY.

BUT YOU'RE OLD ENOUGH NOW, AND I NEED YOU TO UNDERSTAND A FEW THNGS.

SINCE YOU AND FREDDY FIRST CAME HERE, R.A.I.D. AND THE SCHOOL HAVE... HAD AN *ARRANGEMENT.* WE'VE WORKED TOGETHER.

THERE ARE PEOPLE...

I'M SORRY. THIS IS HORRIBLE.

BUT THERE ARE PEOPLE WHO THOUGHT THAT YOU AND FREDDY SHOULD NEVER HAVE COME HERE.

THAT YOU'RE *DANGEROUS.*

AND TO MAKE THIS WORK, I NEED YOU TO... TO KEEP YOUR HEAD DOWN.

TO NOT MAKE A FUSS.

NOT DRAW ALL THIS... *ATTENTION* TO YOUR- SELF.

ATTENTION?

ARE YOU *KIDDING* ME?

ATTENTION?!

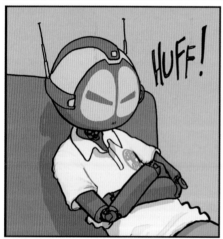

ALEX, CAN YOU COME TO MY OFFICE, PLEASE?

WE NEED TO HAVE A LITTLE TALK.

EVERYONE ELSE – PUT YOUR COATS AND BAGS AWAY AND GET TO YOUR CLASSROOMS, PLEASE.

DID SHE SAY WE SHOULD TAKE OUR COATS OFF, TAIA?

I THINK SHE SAID WE SHOULD TAKE OUR COATS OFF, MIRA.

OKAY! EVERYONE!

COATS OFF!

69

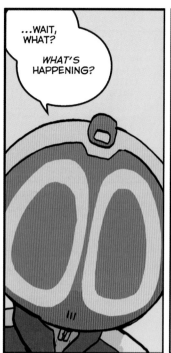

...WAIT, WHAT?

WHAT'S HAPPENING?

I TALKED YOU YOUR MUM.

SHE MADE US ALL NEW SCHOOL JUMPERS!

THEY'RE MAGIC!

THEY'RE NOT MAGIC. THEY'RE WOVEN FROM POLY-CHROMATIC SMART FIBRES.

THEY'RE BASICALLY MAGIC.

CHECK IT OUT.

FSSH!

ALL RIGHT.

THANK YOU, SAMIRA. THANK YOU, TAIA.

EVERYONE, OFF TO CLASSES.

YOU TOO, ALEX.

YOU GUYS, I...

YOU GUYS.

OH GOD, WHAT IS HAPPENING?

IS THIS A NIGHTMARE?

WHY IS EVERYTHING PINK?

CHAPTER

3

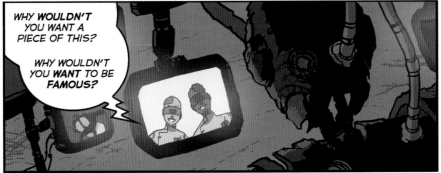

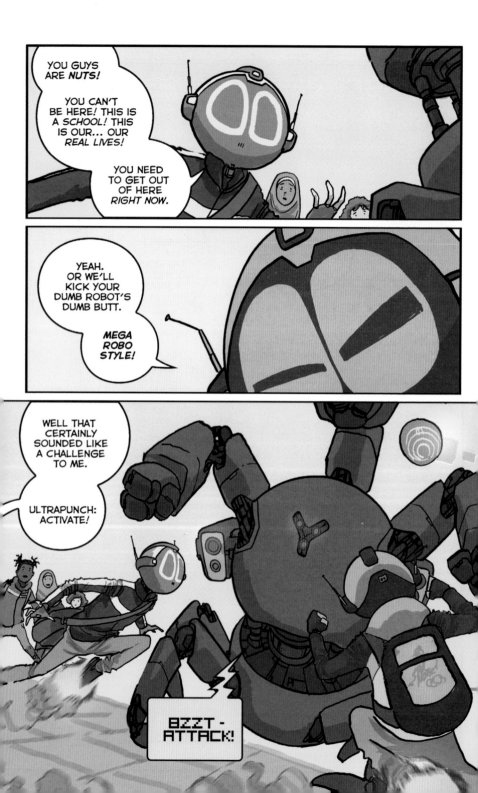

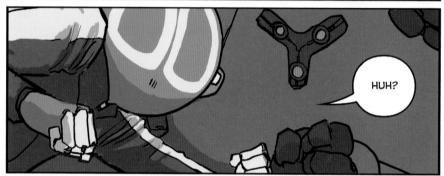

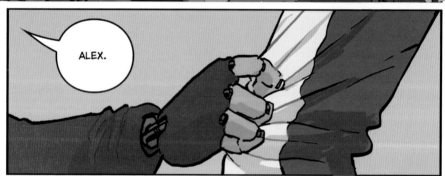

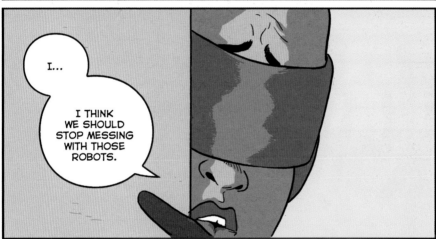

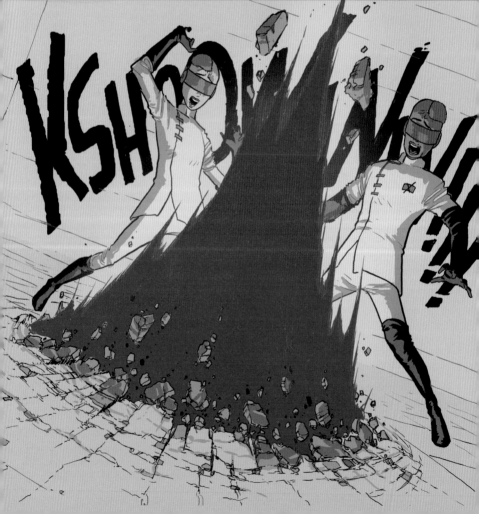

CHAPTER 4

I'M LOOKING OVER SOME OF YOUR BOYS' RECENT MISSION LOGS.

AND I MUST SAY, THE RESULTS ARE...

...WELL, THEY'RE ABOUT WHAT ONE WOULD EXPECT WHEN SENSITIVE SECURITY WORK IS UNDERTAKEN BY *CHILDREN*, I SUPPOSE.

FOR EXAMPLE...

DRILL-MECH

DATA FILES

STATUS: DEACTIVATED

WITH RESPECT, BARONESS FAROOQ... I DON'T SEE THE PROBLEM.

ALEX AND FREDDY'S ASSIGNMENT WAS TO NEUTRALISE THE ROGUE DRILL-MECH.

WHICH THEY *DID.*

INDEED. LEAVING JUST THE SMALL MATTER OF A *COLONY OF DEFECTIVE ROBOTS,* AT LARGE AND UNACCOUNTED FOR, SOMEWHERE *UNDERNEATH THIS CITY.*

AH.

THAT.

BUT THE SHELTER ROBOTS – THEY WERE SMALL. *BROKEN.*

DOMESTIC AND ENTERTAINMENT UNITS, MOSTLY.

ALEX JUDGED THAT THEY DIDN'T REPRESENT A THREAT.

AND FRANKLY, I AGREED.

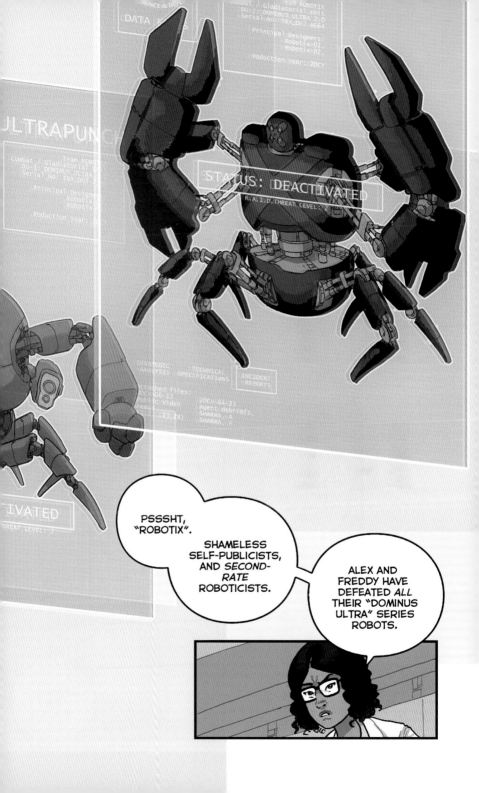

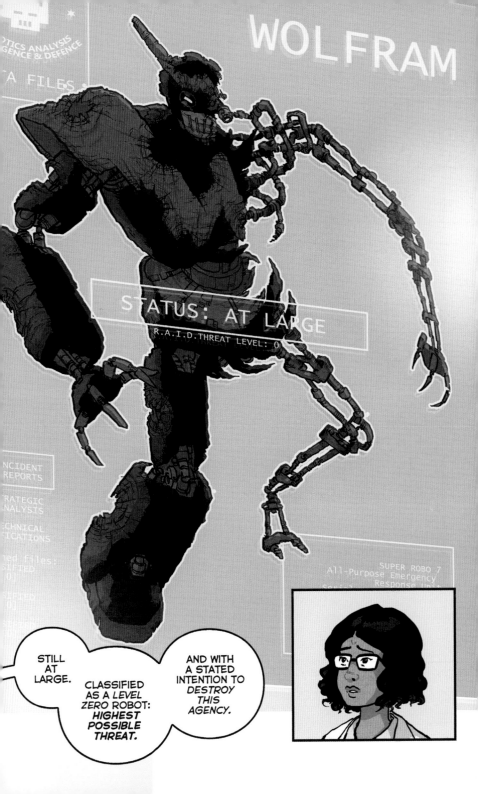

I'VE BEEN READING THE FILES, DOCTOR SHARMA.

HAVE YOU EVEN TOLD THEM?

WHO HE IS?

NO, I...

I WAS WAITING. UNTIL...

UNTIL THEY WERE OLDER.

DOCTOR SHARMA.

I AM NOT A PARENT. I DEFER TO YOUR JUDGEMENT REGARDING YOUR OWN CHILDREN.

I JUST HOPE YOU REALISE HOW MUCH IS RIDING ON THAT JUDGEMENT.

102

CHAPTER 5

SHARMA, ALEX

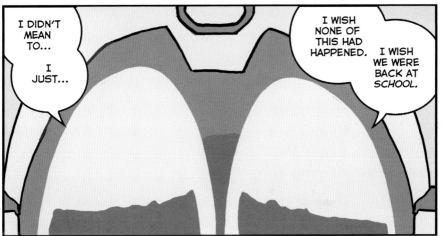

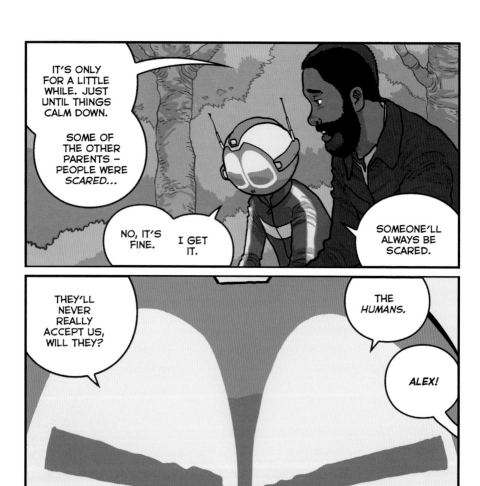

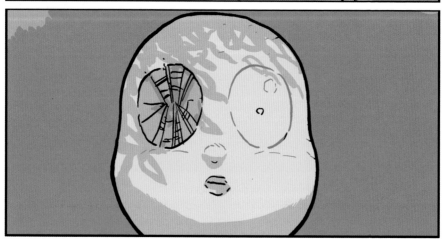

111

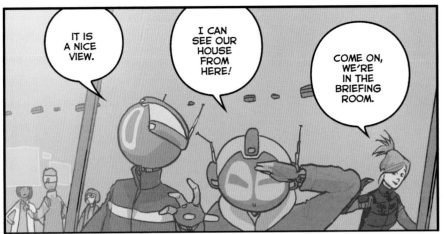

114

THIS MESSAGE CAME ON A PRIVATE CHANNEL. ENCODED.

USUALLY, THEY'RE ALL ABOUT *MAXIMUM PUBLICITY.*

W...WE'RE EMBEDDING A FLIGHT PLAN TO OUR LOCATION...

COME FACE US...

IF YOU D... DARE...

YOU SEE IT, FREDDY?

YEP!

ALEX, FREDDY — WAIT

SOMETHING'S NOT RIGHT HERE — THE ROUTEFINDER'S BEEN ENCODED SO ONLY YOUR SYSTEMS CAN SEE IT.

WE CAN'T TRACK IT — WE DON'T EVEN KNOW HOW THEY WERE ABLE TO *DO* THAT...

APPARENTLY SO.

THIS IS WHERE THEY WANTED US TO COME?

I DON'T GET IT. IT'S...

A DESERTED BUILDING SITE.

WHY ARE WE ON A DESERTED BUILDING SITE?

YOU KNOW AS MUCH AS I DO.

MAYBE THEY WANTED TO HAVE A FIGHT WHERE THERE'S NO ONE AROUND TO GET HURT.

LIKE THEY SUDDENLY CARE.

MAYBE THEY...

HEY!

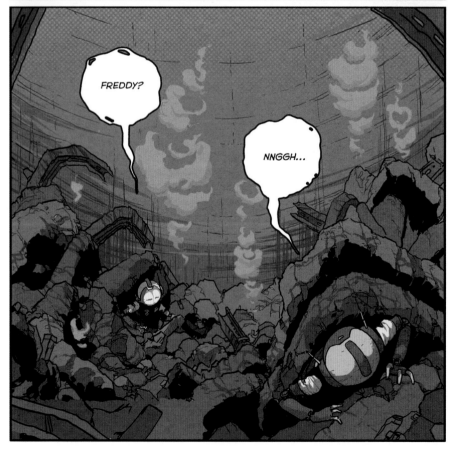

127

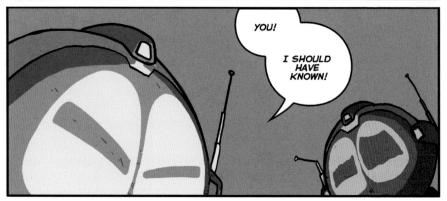

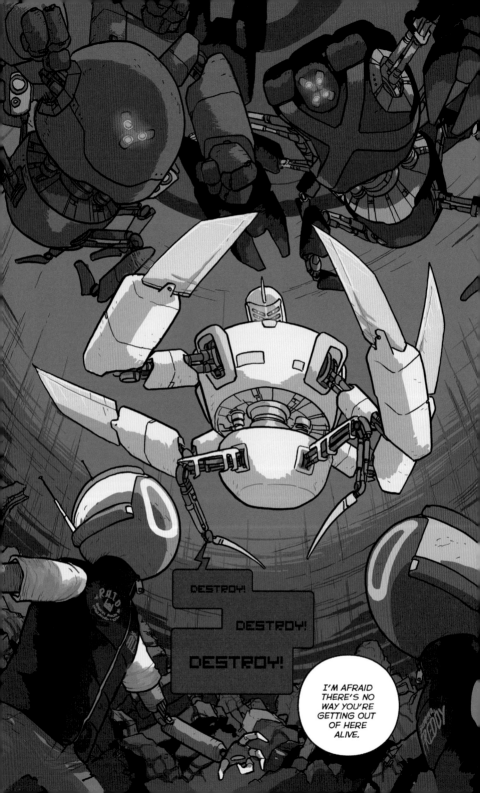

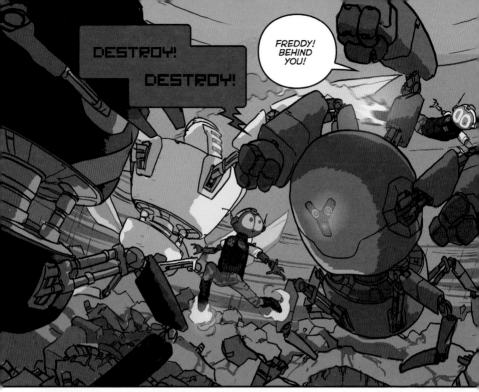

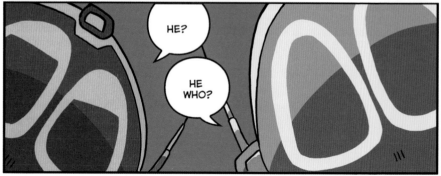

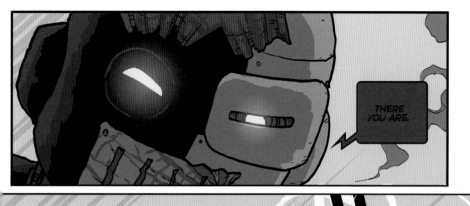

157

STRONG ENOUGH TO CRUSH YOU, LITTLE ROBOTS.

KRANNG!!!

KROOOM!!!

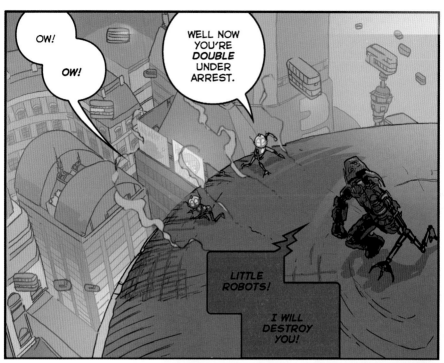

THE END

MEGA ROBO BROS

WILL RETURN IN

MELT DOWN

ALEX

ALEX WAS ALREADY FIVE WHEN HE CAME TO LIVE WITH THE SHARMAS, BUT DOESN'T REMEMBER MUCH OF HIS LIFE BEFORE. AND MAYBE... DOESN'T *WANT* TO REMEMBER.

STRENGTH	
SPEED	
WEAPONRY	
SENTIENCE	

FREDDY

FREDDY WAS ADOPTED BY MICHAEL AND NITA SHARMA WHEN HE WAS JUST A BABY, SO HE'S ONLY EVER KNOWN LIFE AS A KID IN A (RELATIVELY) NORMAL HOME!

STRENGTH	8
SPEED	9+
WEAPONRY	9+
SENTIENCE	9+

R.A.I.
ROBOTICS ANA
INTELLIGENCE & D

DATA FIL

SUSIE

AS WELL AS BEING ALEX AND FREDDY'S OCCASIONAL BABYSITTER, SUSIE NICHOLS IS A HIGHLY TRAINED *R.A.I.D.* FIELD AGENT, ACTING AS THEIR HANDLER ON COMBAT MISSIONS!

STRENGTH	5
SPEED	6
WEAPONRY	7
BABYSITTING	9

THE BARONESS

A HIGH-RANKING GOVERNMENT OFFICIAL WITH SPECIAL OVERSIGHT FOR CYBER-SECURITY, BARONESS FATIMA FAROOQ HEADS UP *R.A.I.D.* WITH A FIRM HAND!

STRENGTH	3
SPEED	4
WEAPONRY	6
AUTHORITY	9

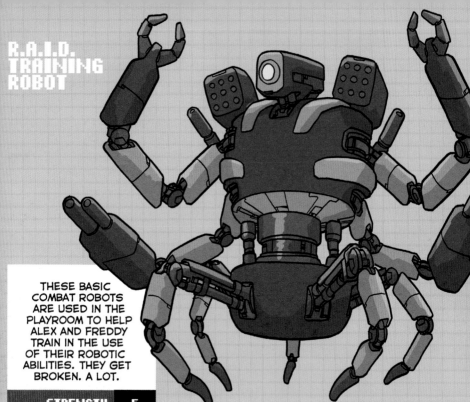

R.A.I.D. TRAINING ROBOT

THESE BASIC COMBAT ROBOTS ARE USED IN THE PLAYROOM TO HELP ALEX AND FREDDY TRAIN IN THE USE OF THEIR ROBOTIC ABILITIES. THEY GET BROKEN. A LOT.

STRENGTH	5
SPEED	5
WEAPONRY	6
SENTIENCE	2

R.A.I.D. SENTRY ROBOT

THESE FLOATING SENTRIES DEFEND SITES OF STRATEGIC IMPORTANCE - INCLUDING *R.A.I.D.* TOWER IN LONDON - FROM ROBOTIC THREATS!

STRENGTH	7
SPEED	5
WEAPONRY	6
SENTIENCE	2

R.A.I.
ROBOTICS AN
INTELLIGENCE &

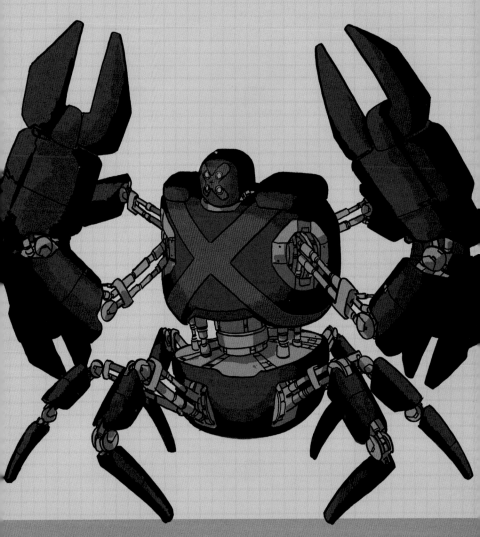

DOMINUS ULTRA 2.0: ULTRAMAXX

ULTRAMAXX'S POWERFUL CRUSHING TITANIUM CLAWS ARE CAPABLE OF CAUSING ENORMOUS DAMAGE – TO OTHER ROBOTS, OR TO LONDON'S STREETS!

STRENGTH	8
SPEED	5
WEAPONRY	6
SENTIENCE	2

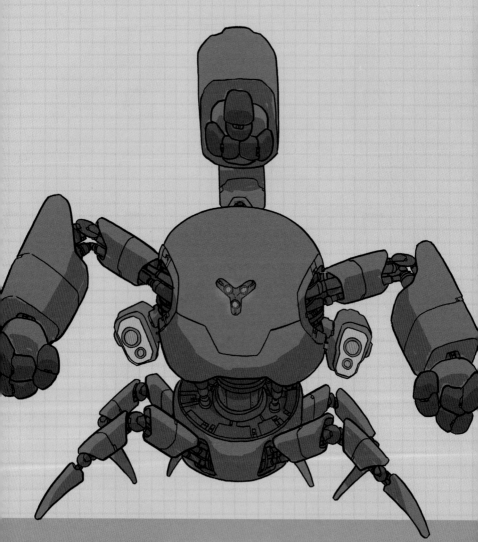

DOMINUS ULTRA 3.0: ULTRAPUNCH

THE LAST AND MOST POWERFUL OF THE *DOMINUS ULTRA* SERIES ROBOTS, ULTRAPUNCH'S GROUND-LOCKING LEGS AND TRIPLE-REINFORCED TITANIUM ARMOUR MADE IT *NIGH-INDESTRUCTIBLE!*

STRENGTH	9
SPEED	4
WEAPONRY	7
SENTIENCE	2

WOLFRAM

POWERFUL AND
DRIVEN BY AN
UNCONTROLLABLE RAGE
BENT ON REVENGE,
WOLFRAM IS THE DEADLIEST
ROBOT ALEX AND FREDDY –
OR THE WORLD – HAVE
EVER FACED!

STRENGTH	9+
SPEED	9+
WEAPONRY	9+
SENTIENCE	6

ZAHRA

ZAHRA ABDIKARÍM IS ONE OF R.A.I.D.'S TOP SCIENTISTS, RESPONSIBLE FOR PROGRAMMING ALEX AND FREDDY'S TRAINING ROUTINES!

STRENGTH	4
SPEED	5
WEAPONRY	2
CODING	9

R.A.I.D. EMPLOYS HUNDREDS OF FIELD AGENTS, EXPERT IN ROBOTICS ENGINEERING, URBAN PEACE-KEEPING AND COMBAT!

R.A.I.D. AGENT

STRENGTH	5
SPEED	5
WEAPONRY	6
INDIVIDUALITY	4

HOW TO DRAW TRIKEY!

1 'TRICERATOPS' MEANS 'THREE-HORNED FACE' - SO START BY DRAWING THREE HORNS!

2 JOIN THEM UP TO MAKE THE *HEAD* SHAPE!

3 ADD CIRCLES FOR THE EYES!

4 DRAW TWO UPSIDE-DOWN TRIANGLES FOR THE JAW!

5 PAC-MAN SHAPES INSIDE THE CIRCLES...

6 .. AND THEN LITTLE CIRCLES INSIDE OF THOSE.

7 LINES STICKING OUT EITHER SIDE...

8 ...AND THEN CURVED LINES GOING UP FROM THERE.

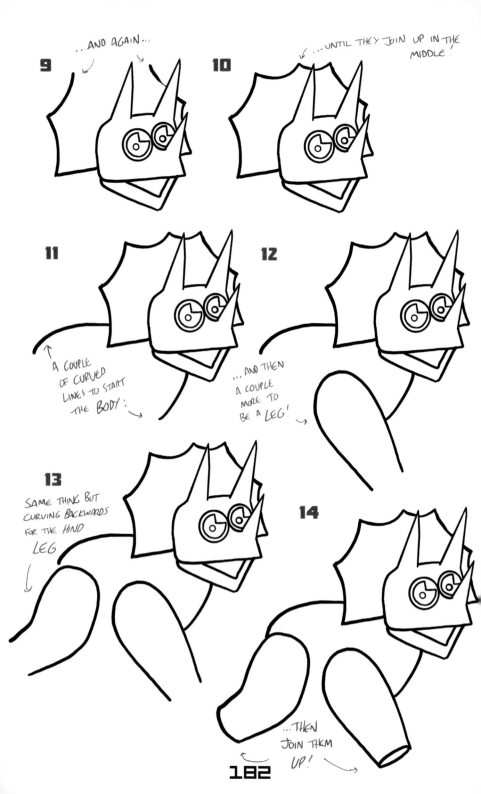

...AND AGAIN...

9

...UNTIL THEY JOIN UP IN THE MIDDLE!

10

11

A COUPLE OF CURVED LINES TO START THE BODY :

12

...AND THEN A COUPLE MORE TO BE A LEG!

13

SAME THING BUT CURVING BACKWARDS FOR THE HIND LEG

14

...THEN JOIN THEM UP!

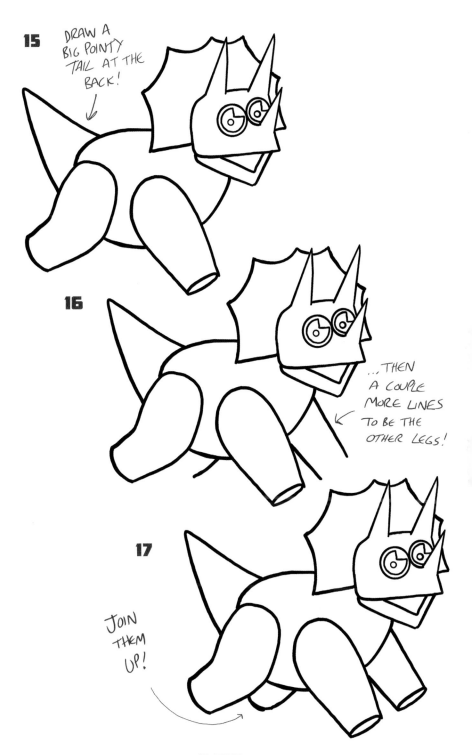

15 DRAW A BIG POINTY TAIL AT THE BACK!

16 ...THEN A COUPLE MORE LINES TO BE THE OTHER LEGS!

17 JOIN THEM UP!

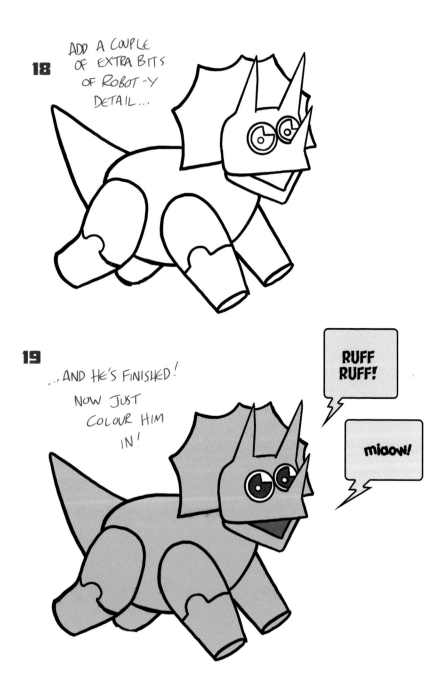

HOW TO DRAW WOLFRAM

1 DRAW A WONKY DIAGONAL SHAPE - LIKE HALF A 'W'

2 DRAW THE HEAD SHAPE AROUND IT.

3 ...THEN ADD A SQUARE UNDERNEATH

4 GIVE HIM AN EYE!

5 ...AND THEN A COUPLE OF CIRCLES TO MAKE THE OTHER EYE!

6 ADD IN A BIT MORE HEAD SHAPE BEHIND

7

.. AND THEN THESE TWO LINES MAKE THE JAW!

8

FOUR STRAIGHT LINES!

9

...AND A LITTLE BOX SHAPE UNDERNEATH, TO START THE NECK!

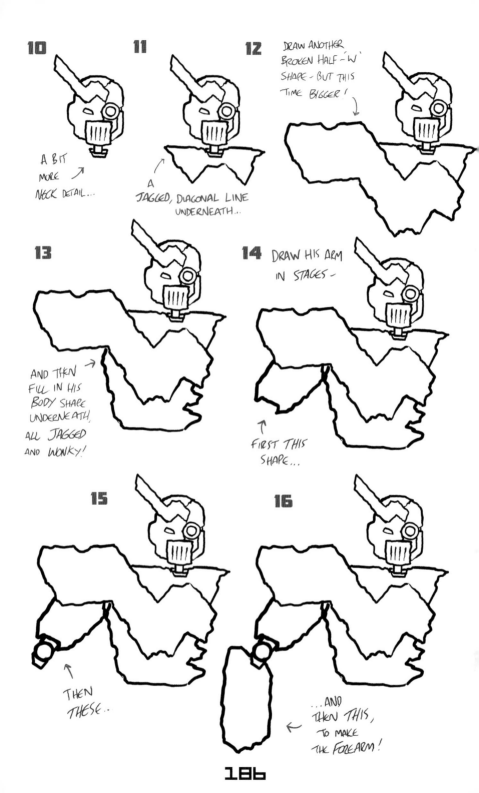

10

A BIT MORE NECK DETAIL...

11

A JAGGED, DIAGONAL LINE UNDERNEATH...

12

DRAW ANOTHER BROKEN HALF - 'W' SHAPE - BUT THIS TIME BIGGER!

13

AND THEN FILL IN HIS BODY SHAPE UNDERNEATH, ALL JAGGED AND WONKY!

14

DRAW HIS ARM IN STAGES -

FIRST THIS SHAPE...

15

THEN THESE...

16

...AND THEN THIS, TO MAKE THE FOREARM!

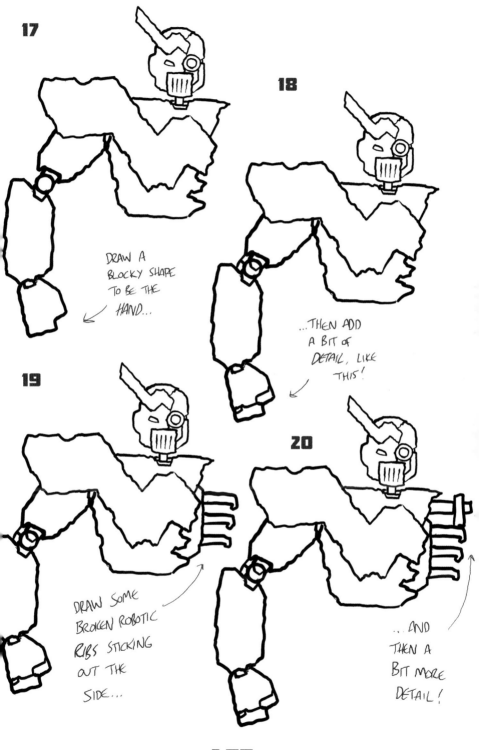

17

DRAW A
BLOCKY SHAPE
TO BE THE
HAND...

18

...THEN ADD
A BIT OF
DETAIL, LIKE
THIS!

19

DRAW SOME
BROKEN ROBOTIC
RIBS STICKING
OUT THE
SIDE...

20

...AND
THEN A
BIT MORE
DETAIL!

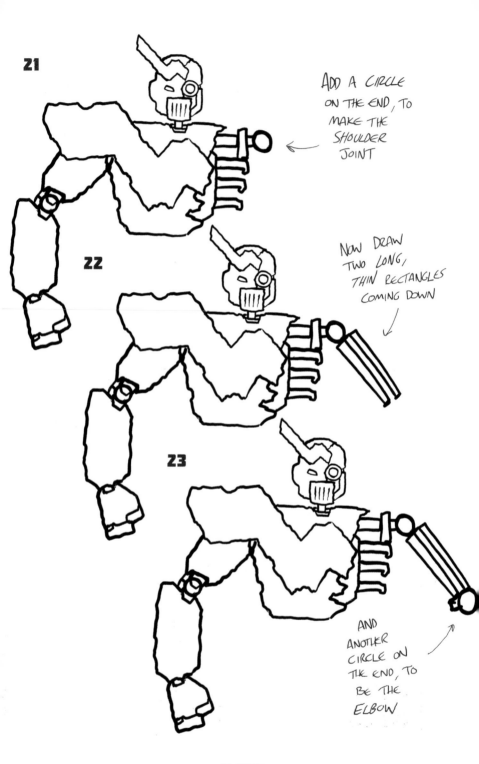

21

ADD A CIRCLE ON THE END, TO MAKE THE SHOULDER JOINT

22

NOW DRAW TWO LONG, THIN RECTANGLES COMING DOWN

23

AND ANOTHER CIRCLE ON THE END, TO BE THE ELBOW

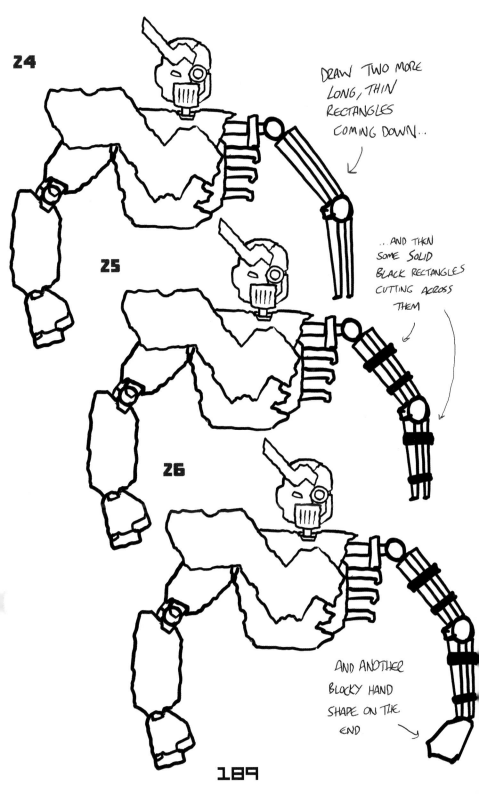

24

DRAW TWO MORE
LONG, THIN
RECTANGLES
COMING DOWN...

25

.. AND THEN
SOME SOLID
BLACK RECTANGLES
CUTTING ACROSS
THEM

26

AND ANOTHER
BLOCKY HAND
SHAPE ON THE
END

189

27

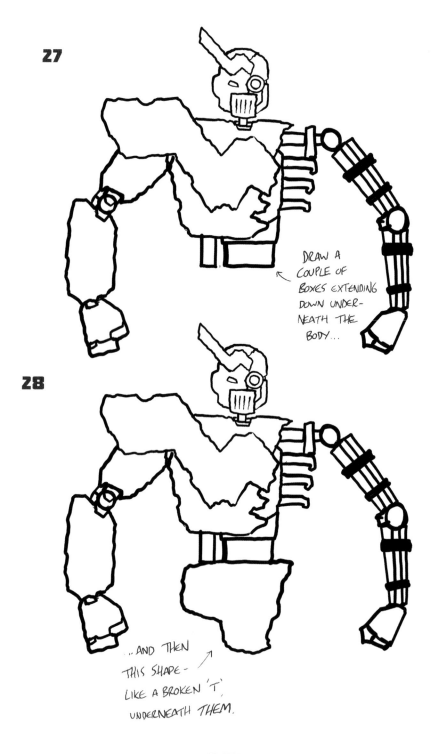

DRAW A COUPLE OF BOXES EXTENDING DOWN UNDERNEATH THE BODY...

28

...AND THEN THIS SHAPE - LIKE A BROKEN 'T', UNDERNEATH THEM.

29 NOW, TO DRAW THE LEGS...

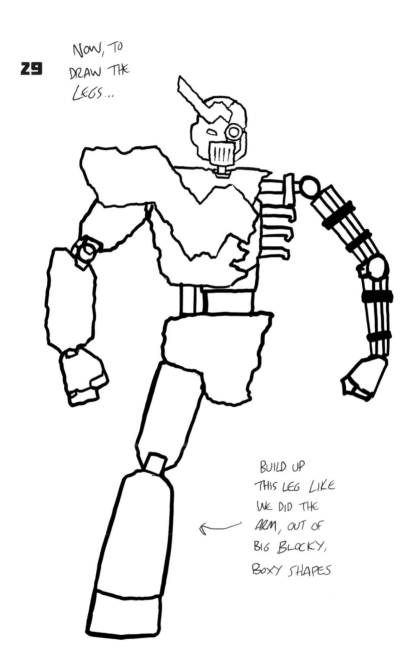

BUILD UP THIS LEG LIKE WE DID THE ARM, OUT OF BIG BLOCKY, BOXY SHAPES

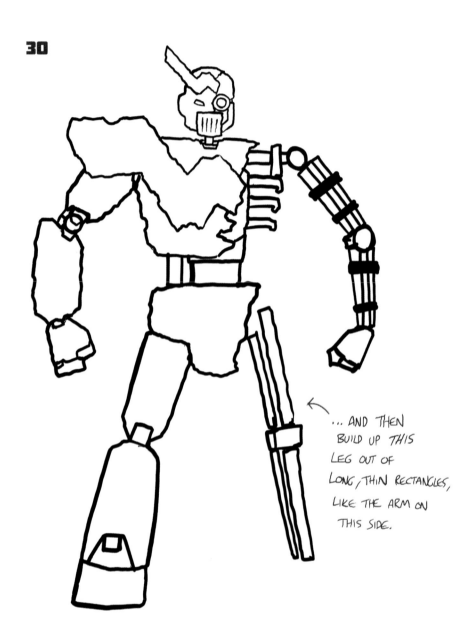

... AND THEN
BUILD UP *THIS*
LEG OUT OF
LONG/THIN RECTANGLES,
LIKE THE ARM ON
THIS SIDE.

31

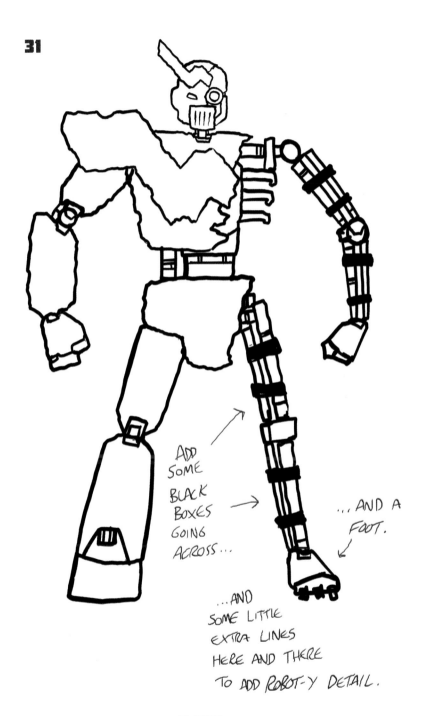

ADD
SOME
BLACK
BOXES
GOING
ACROSS...

...AND A
FOOT.

...AND
SOME LITTLE
EXTRA LINES
HERE AND THERE
TO ADD ROBOT-Y DETAIL.

32

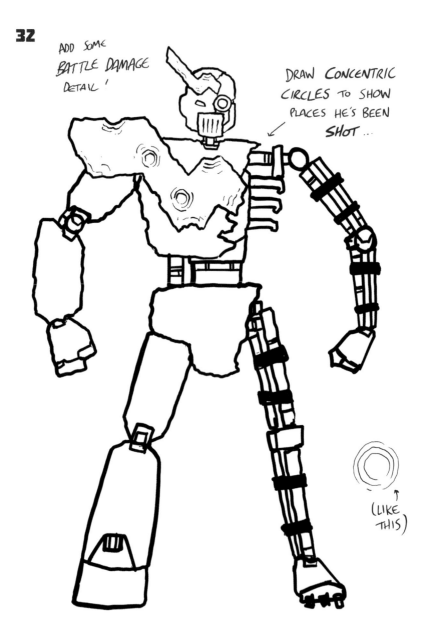

ADD SOME BATTLE DAMAGE DETAIL!

DRAW CONCENTRIC CIRCLES TO SHOW PLACES HE'S BEEN SHOT...

(LIKE THIS)

33

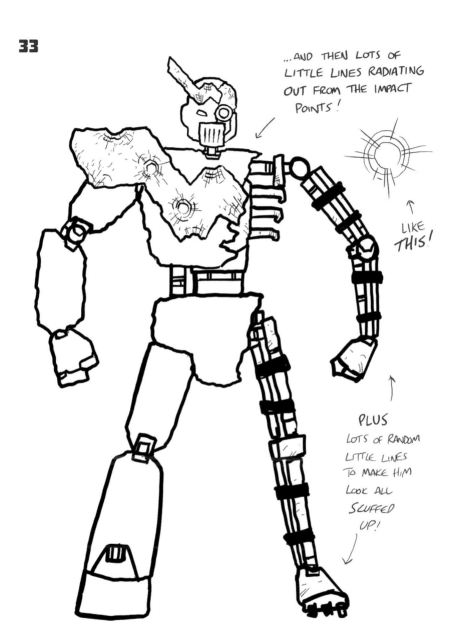

...AND THEN LOTS OF LITTLE LINES RADIATING OUT FROM THE IMPACT POINTS!

LIKE *THIS!*

PLUS LOTS OF RANDOM LITTLE LINES TO MAKE HIM LOOK ALL SCUFFED UP!

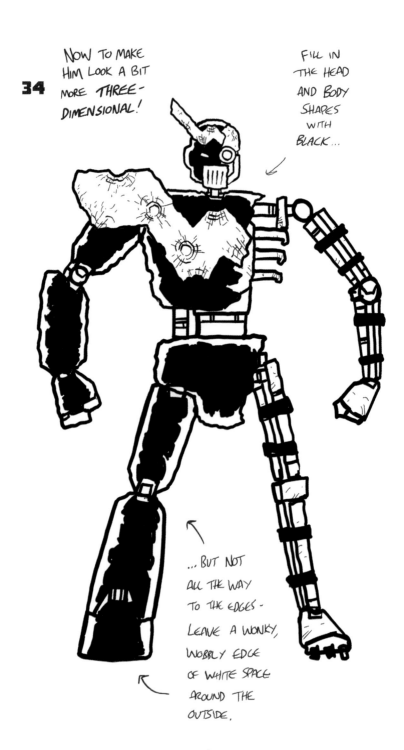

34 NOW TO MAKE HIM LOOK A BIT MORE *THREE-DIMENSIONAL!*

FILL IN THE HEAD AND BODY SHAPES WITH BLACK...

...BUT NOT ALL THE WAY TO THE EDGES - LEAVE A WONKY, WOBBLY EDGE OF WHITE SPACE AROUND THE OUTSIDE.

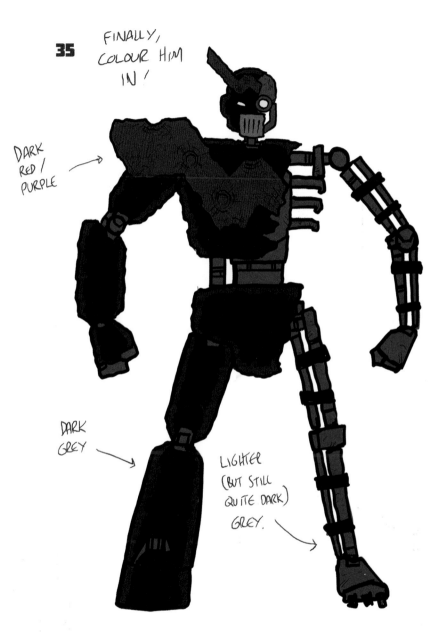

35 FINALLY, COLOUR HIM IN!

DARK RED / PURPLE

DARK GREY

LIGHTER (BUT STILL QUITE DARK) GREY.

TA-DAH! ALL DONE, AND READY... TO DESTROY HUMANITY!

THE WORLD ACCORDING TO FREDDY!

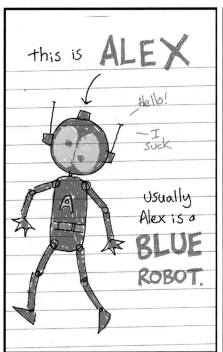

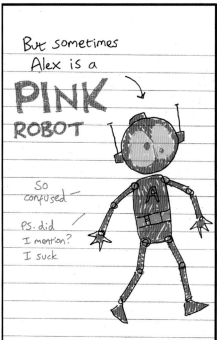

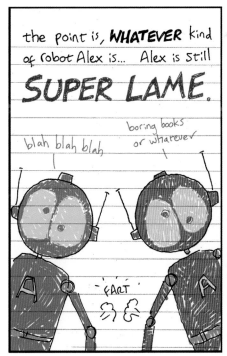

Even though me and Alex work for **R.A.I.D.**, they do not actually **PAY** us?

ZAP!

ZAP!

to fix this **UNJUST** and **PROBABLY ILLEGAL** situation, I have the following **DEMANDS:**

ON STRIKE

1: one **MILLION POUNDS!** £

no wait,

2: **TWO MILLION!** £

3: my own **OFFICE!** which is full of **TRAMPOLINES!**

4: a **SPORTS CAR** with my **FACE** on it!

5: all the **HOT DOGS** and/or **PIZZA** I can **EAT!**

THIS IS A SECURE OFFICE.

HOW DID YOU EVEN GET *IN* HERE?

THEY ARE *REASONABLE* DEMANDS!

When I am not going on **AWESOME MISSIONS** and **SAVING THE WORLD** and stuff, I have to go... to SCHOOL.

SCHOOL.

School is a place you have to go **EVERY DAY** and wear **UNIFORMS** and sit in **ROWS** and be forced to endure **CRUEL** AND **UNUSUAL PUNISHMENTS.**

by which I mean **MATHS.**

I think school should teach us **USEFUL STUFF** instead, like how to **START REVOLUTIONS,** and **DO MAGIC,** and also maybe **SWORD-FIGHTING?**

...THIS CONCLUDES MY PRESENTATION.

WOO!

YEAH!

SWORDS!

THANK YOU, FREDDY.

I THINK THAT MIGHT BE OUR LAST SHOW AND TELL FOR A WHILE.

FREDDY VS SCHOOL

&

FREDDY AND THE NEW KID

MY NAME IS FREDDY.
I LIVE WITH MY MUM & DAD.
I GO TO SCHOOL.
I'M AN AWESOME ROBOT!

Okay humans, listen up! Here are the . . .

TOP THINGS YOU SHOULD PROBABLY KNOW ABOUT ME!

1 My name is *FREDDY.*

2 I live in London with my mum and dad.

3 I go to school.

4 I have a big brother called Alex.

5 Oh yeah, the MAIN thing: I am an

AWESOME ROBOT!

. . . I should maybe have started with that?

I have many **AMAZING ROBOTIC ABILITIES.**

I can . . .

FLY!

FWOOSH!!

And also I have

LASERS!

KZOW!

KZOW!